JED PASCOE'S

THE FUNNY SIDE OF

50

FOR HIM

Dad,
Happy Birthday,
Love
Charlotte x.

First Published in Great Britain by
Powerfresh Limited
3 Gray Street
Northampton
England
NN1 3QQ

Telephone 0604 30996 Country Code 44
Facsimile 0604 21013

THE FUNNY SIDE OF 50 FOR HIM
ISBN 1 874125 12 0

Printed in Britain by Avalon Print Ltd., Northampton.

SURPRISE !!

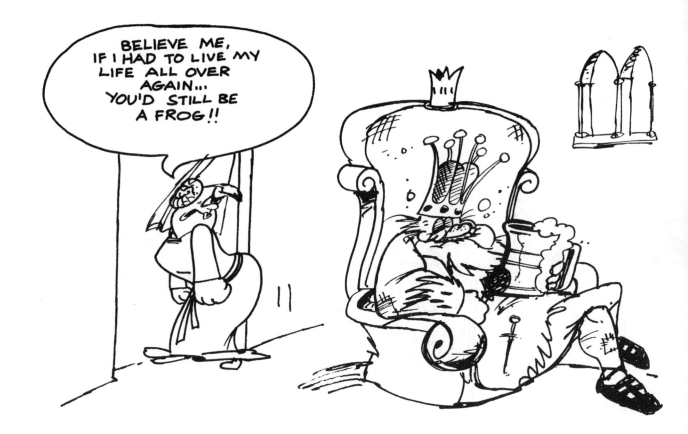

YOU MUST LEARN TO RELAX ...

I'M LOOKING FORWARD TO THIS NEW-FOUND FREEDOM
OF THE WAVES... WHAT TIME DOES THE TIDE COME IN?

THE GOOD NEWS IS THAT NOW I'M FIFTY, I'VE GIVEN UP SMOKING, DRINKING AND HIGH-RISK FOODS
THE BAD NEWS IS THAT WHEN I WAKE UP IN THE MORNING, I KNOW THAT'S AS GOOD AS I'M GOING TO FEEL ALL DAY...

YOU'RE GETTING OLD WHEN YOU START FANCYING THE MUMS...

I'LL HAVE TO GO - I THINK JOHN IS HAVING A MID-LIFE CRISIS...

I'M HOPING THEY'LL MATE...

JUST IN CASE YOU HAVE ONE OF YOUR HOT FLUSHES
IN THE MIDDLE OF THE NIGHT...

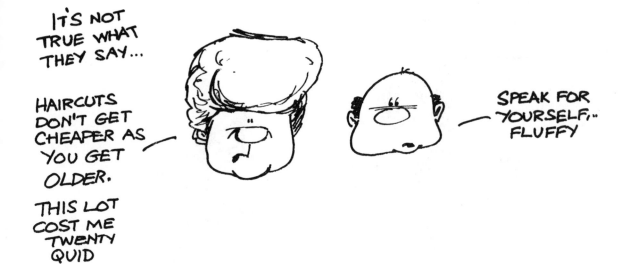

The peril of only cleaning the hair from a plug-hole once every twenty years...

IF CLIFF RICHARD CAN DO IT AT HIS AGE.. THEN SO CAN I!

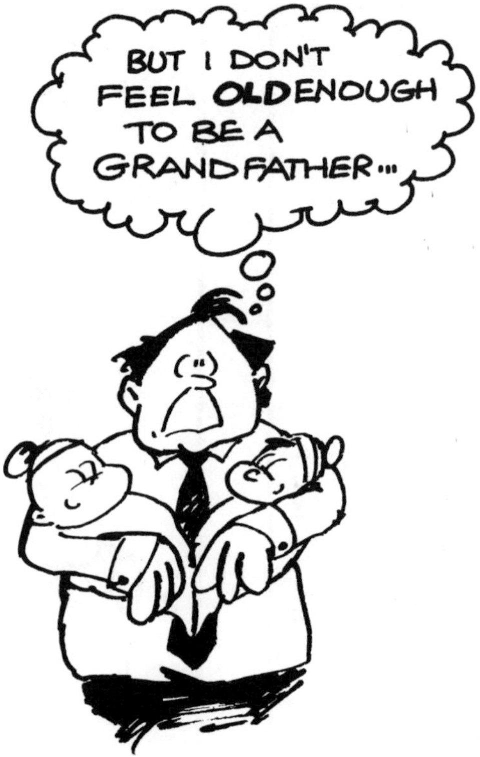
BUT I DON'T FEEL OLD ENOUGH TO BE A GRANDFATHER...

"...BUT, MR. SMITHSON," SURELY WE SHOULD AT LEAST TRY TO FIND A TELEPHONE BEFORE HUDDLING TOGETHER FOR WARMTH?

"...AND WHOSE LITTLE HUSBAND ARE YOU?"

JED PASCOE
NATIONAL AND INTERNATIONAL AWARD WINNING CARTOONIST.
LIVING PROOF THAT EMPTY VESSELS MAKE MOST NOISE..
TOTALLY CONFUSED BY LIFE, HE LIVES MAINLY IN HIS BELEAGURED IMAGINATION — WHICH IS ENOUGH TO CONFUSE ANYONE. AND STILL LOOKING FOR FAME AND FORTUNE, IF ANYONE OUT THERE IS INTERESTED.